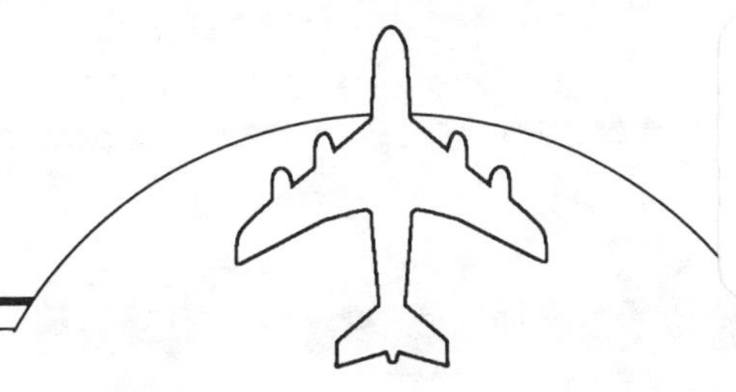

Bernoulli's Book

Written and Illustrated
by B.K. Hixson

Salt Lake City, UT 84115 • (801) 466-1172

Dedication

For Meryl Mills

Because he has mastered the landing of small aircraft under EFK (extremely full kidney) conditions.

For Bob Harney

Because he is the only person I know who will fly to Chicago and back to southern Idaho without ever climbing higher than 50 feet. Also, for his innovative use of U.S. Forest Service markers for aerial navigation.

For Eldon Evans

Because he is crazy enough to fly with Harney.

For Bob Carpenter

Because he is a minister up in Alaska who uses his flying skills to remind unsuspecting visitors of their (immediate) need of a savior.

Introduction

Greetings!

Section 1

This book is broken into three sections the first section deals with the idea that there is air surrounding the earth and this air creates pressure that can move things, and is generally responsible for some pretty unusual phenomena. Unusual, that is, until you start to think about air in a little different manner.

We cover three basic ideas in this section and they are: Air pushes downward, creating a pressure on all things. Air pressure changes all the time and can be measured. And, most importantly, air gives rise to Air Pressure Rule # 1 : Science Never Sucks.

Section 2

This section is about a man named Bernoulli who was an Italian physicist that figured out the physics behind flight. The law is fairly simple to understand, and even easier to illustrate with the activities in this section. He discovered that **the faster a fluid travels over a surface, the less time it has to push on that surface**. Air behaves just like a fluid so there is a direct correlation.

Section 3

Finally, it's time to apply everything that we have been learning into gizmos that fly. This section contains patterns and information about how to make paper airplanes, water driven rockets, and solid fuel rockets. The best part of the book.

Legal Stuff

For further information please contact us at:

The Wild Goose Company
375 W. Whitney Ave.
Salt Lake City Utah 84115
801-466-1172

Table of Contents

Scientific Method

1. Think of an Idea

The first thing that you will need to do is think of an idea for what you will try to explain or do in your experiment, or just something you may want to study. The best way to get started is to adapt an existing experiment in your own unique way.

2. Research Your Topic

Find out what is already known about the topic, and see what you can add to the general body of knowledge.

3. Plan Your Experiment

This section is also called the procedure. You make a game plan of when, where, how, what, and why you are going to do what it is that you are going to do.

4. Experiment

Party time. This is where you get right down to the nitty gritty of doing the experiment, collecting the data, rolling up the sleeves and diving right into the fray.

5. Collect and Record Data

This is all the information that you are seeking, including charts, data tables and records of observations.

6. Come to a Conclusion

Compile the data that you have collected, evaluate the results, come to a conclusion, write a law describing what you observed, and collect your Nobel Prize.

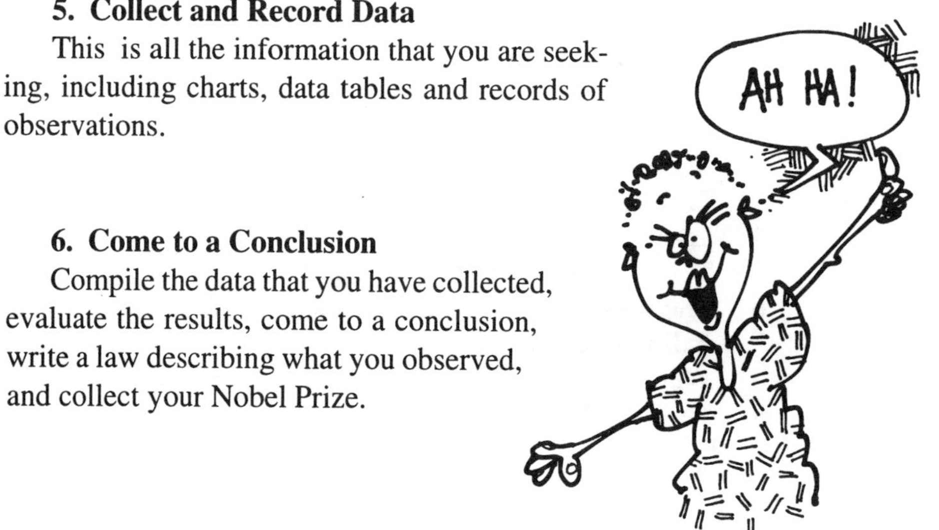

Lab Safety Skills

In every lab class there is always the danger that you may expose yourself to injury. The chemicals and equipment that you use and the way that you use them are very important, not only for your safety but for the safety of those working around you. Please observe the following rules at all times. Failure to do so increases your risk of accident.

1. Goggles.

Goggles should always be worn when chemicals are being heated or mixed. This will protect your eyes from chemicals that spatter or explode. Running water should be available. If you happen to get some chemical in your eye, flush thoroughly with water for 15 minutes. If irritation develops, contact a physician. Take this information with you.

2. Smelling Chemicals.

If you need to smell a chemical to identify it, hold it 6 inches away from your nose and wave your hand over the opening of the container toward your nose. This will "waft" some of the fumes toward your nose without exposing you to a large dose of anything noxious.

3. Chemical Contact With Skin.

Your kit contains protective gloves to wear whenever you are handling chemicals. If you do happen to spill a chemical on your skin, flush the area with water for 15 minutes. If irritation develops, contact a physician. Take the instructions for this kit with you.

4. Clean up all Messes Immediately.

This is no time to be a pig. Your lab area should be spotless when you start experimenting and spotless when you leave. If not, clean it.

5. Proper Disposal of Poisons.

If a poisonous substance is used or formed during the experiments in this lab, the book will tell you. These must be handled according to the directions in the lab guide.

Lab Safety Skills

6. No Eating During the Lab.

When you eat, you run the risk of internalizing poison. This is never done unless the lab calls for it. Make sure your hands and lab area are clean.

7. Horse play Out.

Horseplay can lead to chemical spills, accidental fires, broken containers, and damaged equipment. Never throw anything to another person; be careful where you put your hands and arms; and no wrestling, punching, or shoving in the lab. Save that for when you get older and start dating.

8. Fire.

If there is a fire in the room notify the person in charge immediately. If they are not in the room and the fire is manageable, smother the fire with a blanket or use an extinguisher in an emergency and send someone to find an adult. REMEMBER: Stop, Drop, and Roll!

9. Better Safe Than Sorry.

If you have questions, or if you are not sure how to handle a particular chemical, procedure, or part of an experiment, ask for help from your instructor or an adult. If you do not feel comfortable doing something, then don't do it. If there is any concern upon chemical exposure, contact a physician.

Air Pressure

There is air all around us.

This section deals with the fact that there is air piled on top of us and that same air, being piled on top of us, pushes on all things. We call this air pressure.

To start at the beginning, we need to prove that there is air pressure, and to do that, we need to understand how it got here in the first place. In the illustration to the right we see that we are surrounded by the atmosphere, that proverbial "sea of air." Actually, that's really a good term as we shall demonstrate later in the book. This atmosphere extends up 50 miles or so. Traces of the atmosphere have been found as high as 100 miles, but 50 tends to be the recognized value. Not having been to the edge of the atmosphere lately, we'll take their word for it. Enough said, there is air.

This air pushes downward, creating a pressure on all things.

Essentially, what this means is we have 50 miles of air pushing down on us. As you get higher and higher in altitude, the air pressure gets lower because there is actually less air on top of you. But for our purposes, this change makes about as much difference as if you were to argue if it hurt less to get run over by a dump truck versus a loaded semi.

Air pressure changes all the time and can be measured.

This air pushes on, under, and around all things with a force of 14.7 pounds per square inch at sea level, less if you are up in the air a little bit. Because we have this constant pressure, we can do things to change it inside or outside objects. These differences in air pressure account for winds, some kinds of storms, and the interesting phenomena that you are going to investigate. Air pressure is changed by heating the air, cooling it, or causing it to move over a surface.

Don't be fooled...

We will deal with the applications of putting these differences to work later. For now, your job is to understand that there is air pressure, and differences in air pressure can push things up, down, and over. It is important to remember that it is a push, because you will be tempted to guess that things are sucked into other containers, and this is not possible because...

Rule # 1 : Science Never Sucks

The Waitress Trick

the concept

An index card is placed over a drinking cup two thirds full of water. When the cup is inverted, the card stays attached to the bottom of the cup and the water remains inside.

the materials

1 drinking cup, any size (clear is best)
1 4" x 6" index card
water

the experiment

1. Fill the drinking glass two thirds to three fourths full with water. Ask the kids to examine the top of the glass to make sure that nothing sticky has been deviously placed there by the science gremlins.

2. Hand the index card to a student for examination. Elicit that there are no sticky substances on the card. Place the card on top of the glass.

3. Place your hand over the index card and invert the glass and the card together.

4. Remove the hand that is on top of the glass. The glass should stay in place, and this should not amaze anyone. Now hang on to the top of the glass and remove the hand that is under the card. The water should remain in the glass. This will amaze at least a couple of the munchkins.

5. You can either place your hand on the card and flip the glass over again or, if you are brave and have quick wrists, just right the card and glass quickly. You may be able to flip the card and glass over again immediately without the use of your other hand. Have a garbage can or tub ready, just in case. For effect, have one of your students sit directly under the glass on a chair, looking straight up as you do this experiment. There is no scientific foundation for this, but the entertainment value is wonderful.

the explanation

As discussed in the introduction to this section, air pressure is pushing on all sides of the glass and the card. The only place where there is a difference of pressure is directly under the opening to the glass. The water weighs a pound or two at best, and the air pressure is exerting anywhere from 14 to 14.7 pounds per square inch on the bottom of the card. I ask the kids who would win, the 14 pounds or the two pounds. The card eventually falls off because it buckles as it absorbs water. This buckling breaks the seal that is created on the bottom of the glass, and the water is pulled out by gravity.

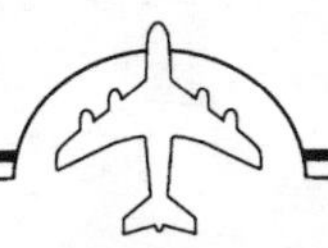

Napkin Preserver

the concept

A dry napkin is wadded up and placed in the bottom of a dry drinking glass. The glass is pushed, open end first, straight down into the water until it is submerged. When the napkin and glass are pulled from the water, the napkin remains dry.

the materials

1 drinking glass
1 napkin
water
1 large container that will hold water (aquarium)

the experiment

1. Take the napkin and have the kids examine it. They will determine that it is dry.

2. Wad said napkin into a little ball and place it inside the glass.

3. Invert the glass and slowly lower it into the aquarium until the napkin and the glass are both completely under water. Remove the glass from the water.

4. Have the kids examine the napkin and determine that it is still dry.

the explanation

This experiment demonstrates that air does indeed take up space. As the glass is submerged into the container, the air inside the glass displaces (or pushes away) the water in the tub. Because the water is displaced, the napkin remains dry. It just doesn't get any simpler than that.

If the kids are having a hard time with the fact that air does take up space, simply have them place their hands on their chests, fingers spread. Ask them to inhale, hold their breath, and then exhale. Ask them if they think that air takes up space.

The Fountain Bath

the concept

The student blows as much air through a straw into a bottle three fourths full of water as is physically possible. When they release the straw, a stream of water shoots up into the air. May get the kids wet, especially if you don't tell them what is going to happen... might have an idea here.

the materials

1 drinking straw
1 2 liter pop bottle
1 #3, one hole stopper or lump of clay
water

the experiment

1. Undress a straw and insert it in the stopper or wrap a lump of clay around the middle of it. When you are all done the straw should look like it has a growth in its midsection.

2. Fill the pop bottle three fourths full with water. With this experiment, you find that the more air you have in the bottle the better the experiment will work. There is a limit to this though; the bottom end of the straw still needs to be in the water.

3. Have the kid blow as much air as is possible into the bottle. When he can't force any more air into it, have him remove his mouth, which releases the pressure on the bottle. Water should shoot out the top of the straw, at least twelve inches. A big kid can get the fountain close to two feet as long as his nose doesn't get in the way.

the explanation

As the bottle is filled with air, the pressure inside increases. When the pressure is released at the top, the air inside the bottle pushes down on the water, forcing it up into and out the straw. This usually soaks the kid. Good fun.

Squished Jug

the concept

A plastic milk jug is filled to capacity with water and has a stopper with a glass tube and rubber tubing inserted in the mouth. The whole contraption is inverted over something that will catch the water. As the air evacuates, the jug collapses under the pressure of the air.

the materials

1 one gallon, plastic milk jug
1 #7, one-hole stopper or a lump of clay
1 6" piece of glass tubing or a straw
1 18" piece of rubber tubing
1 tub to catch the water
water

the experiment

1. Fill the milk jug full with water.

2. Slip the glass tubing into the one-hole stopper or lump of clay. If you are using a stopper, a little bit of glycerine will make the glass tubing slide right in. Then, attach the rubber tubing to the end of the glass tubing.

3. Insert the stopper, with the tubing attached, into the jug. Then, hold the tubing up over the container that is going to hold the water as it runs out. Let the jug empty.

the explanation

As the water in the jug empties out due to the force of gravity, it is creating a space of lower pressure inside the jug. We are taking away the water, but not replacing it with anything else. The air pressure on the outside of the jug remains the same, and this difference between the outside and the inside is what pushes the sides of the jug in.

The same activity can be done by putting a cup of water into an empty, metal paint thinner can. Set the can on a burner with the cap off and get the water inside boiling. Remove the can when it is boiling and cap it immediately. As the air inside cools and contracts, it requires less space. This reduces the inside air pressure, and the air pressure outside pushes the sides of the can inward.

A third option is to use the tall, 16 oz. aluminum cans (beer cans seem to be thinner and therefore work better for this experiment). Heat the can the same way that you did with the paint thinner can. Remove the can and place it upside down in a pie tin filled with cold water, ice water, if you have it. The can will be crushed as the air inside cools.

Thirsty Tubes

the concept

A test tube with a one hole stopper and glass tubing is placed in a bath of boiling water. After several minutes, the tube is removed from the boiling water and inverted into a bath of cold water. The water from the bath rises into the test tube.

the materials

1 pyrex test tube
1 test tube holder
1 #1, one-hole stopper or lump of clay
1 drinking straw or piece of glass tubing
2 1000 ml beakers or water containers
1 hot plate

the experiment

1. Place a small amount of water in the test tube and seal it with the stopper and glass tubing apparatus. Use the illustration to the right as a guide. Fill one beaker with water and ice, the second with water only.

2. Place the beaker with the water only on the hot plate and bring it to a boil. The test tube with the stopper should be in this beaker heating with the water. Heat the test tube in the boiling water for three to four minutes.

3. Using the test tube clamp, remove the test tube from the boiling water and hold it upside down in the beaker of water with ice. Observe the reaction.

the explanation

The reason the water rises into the test tube is a difference of air pressure. This is a take off on the previous experiment. As the hot air in the test tube is cooled, it contracts, taking up less space, i.e. reducing the air pressure inside the tube. The air pressure pushing down on the surface of the water is responsible for pushing the water up into the tube until an equilibrium is established.

Remember, science never sucks. It will push and pull but never, ever suck.

Vertical Flush

the concept

The bottom of a pie tin is just barely covered with water and a candle is placed in the middle. The candle is lit and a drinking glass is placed over the candle. As the flame is extinguished, water is pushed up into the glass.

the materials

1 pie tin
1 votive candle
1 drinking glass (the taller the better)
matches
water
1 bottle of food coloring

the experiment

1. Put just enough water in the pie tin to cover the bottom so that no dry spots exist.

2. Place two or three drops of food coloring in the water and swirl it around. The food coloring is strictly for effect. If you do not have it, the experiment will proceed as described.

3. Place the candle in the middle of the pie tin and light it. Place the glass over the top of the candle and observe what happens. If you have trouble with the glass getting stuck to the bottom of the pie tin, interrupting the experiment, place a penny under the edge of the glass to prop it up a titch.

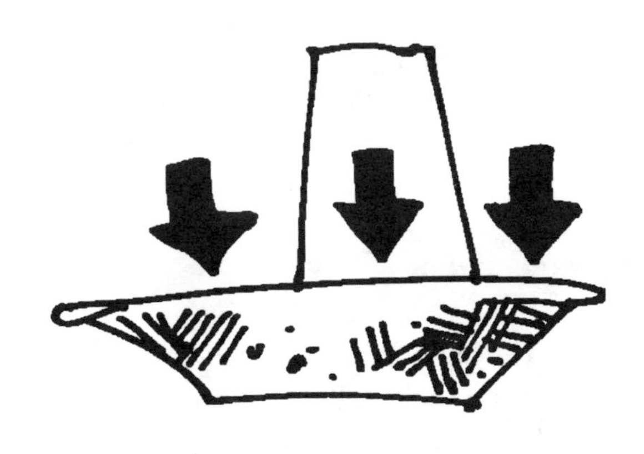

the explanation

When the glass is placed over the candle, the air inside is trapped. It is a closed system. This is pictured in the middle over there. As the candle burns the air trapped inside the glass, the air pressure inside is reduced. The air pressure outside remains the same, so that water is pushed up into the glass. Illustrated for your understanding in the bottom right part of the page. Remember, no sucking.

Hungry Pickle Jar

the concept

A water balloon is placed on top of a pickle jar (or any other kind of jar, for that matter). The balloon is about twice the size of the diameter of the jar opening. When a student tries to push the balloon into the container, it will not budge. A piece of paper towel is lit on fire and dropped into the jar, and the balloon is placed over the jar and miraculously pushed inside.

the materials

1 wide mouth (pickle) jar
1 water balloon
matches
paper towel

the experiment

1. Fill the water balloon up so that it is almost twice the size of the opening of the jar.
2. Place the balloon on top of the jar and try your best to push the balloon into the jar with a flat hand. No squeezing. It won't go because there is air inside the jar pushing back on the balloon.
3. Remove the balloon, set it on the table, and loosely twist a piece of paper towel so that it looks like a doobie. Or, for you non-60's types, a paper cigar. Light it on fire and drop it inside the pickle jar.
4. Place the balloon on top of the jar and observe what happens.

the explanation

The balloon acts as a seal for the jar. No air can get in when the balloon is on top. As the air inside the jar burns, the pressure inside is reduced. A partial vacuum is created. Because there is now a difference in air pressure from the inside of the pickle jar and the outside, the air on the outside pushes the balloon into the jar. Don't forget Rule #1.

If that explanation doesn't wash, tell the kids that the air inside the jar is burned up, making room for the balloon. To remove the balloon, simply place a straw down the side of the jar and pull the balloon and the straw out together. The straw acts as a valve, allowing air to rush down into the pickle jar to compensate for the volume of water that is being removed.

Huevos Extraordinaire

the concept

A peeled, hard boiled egg is placed on top of a juice jar that has an opening that is just a little too small for the egg to fit through. Three matches are placed in the end of the egg and are lit. When the egg is replaced, it is pushed into the bottle.

the materials

1 juice jar
1 hard boiled egg
box of matches (wooden work best)

the experiment

1. Peel a hard boiled egg and place it on top of an empty, clean juice jar. Without breaking the egg, try your best to squish it into the jar. Won't go because the jar is full of air, which takes up space and resents getting squished so it squishes back. If this sounds like an adaptation of the previous experiment, you are exactly correct.

2. Remove the egg. Insert three wooden matches in the end of the egg. Light the matches and quickly place the egg, match end first, on the bottle. The matches need to be inside the bottle for this experiment to work. Observe the reaction.

the explanation

The egg acts as a seal for the jar. No air can get in. As the air inside the jar burns, the pressure inside is reduced. A partial vacuum is created. Because there is now a difference in air pressure from the inside of the juice jar and the outside, the air on the outside pushes the egg into the jar.

You are now posed with another small problem. How do you get the egg out of the jar? Take a deep breath, tip the jar up so that the egg rests against the mouth, and blow quickly into the jar. The musty, old, smells-like-burned-paper egg will pop into your mouth. Fun, huh? And it tastes really good, too.

The reason this works is the short burst of air increases the air pressure inside the jar temporarily. The difference in air pressure, the greater being on the inside rather than the outside for once, pushes the egg back out of the opening. It may be possible to do this experiment a couple of times, but the egg tends to disintegrate with all this pushing and pulling, which is why I prefer the water balloon.

Impossible Balloon

the concept

The students are asked to try to inflate a balloon that is inside a pop bottle. Good for at least one aneurysm.

the materials

1 rubber balloon
1 plastic pop bottle
1 set of lungs

the experiment

1. Wiggle a normal, everyday rubber balloon inside a pop bottle.

2. Fold the opening of the balloon around the mouth of the bottle and attempt to inflate the balloon inside the bottle. No bug eyes.

the explanation

The balloon seals the inside of the bottle. No air can get in and no air can get out of the bottle. As you attempt to inflate the balloon, you are trying to actually increase the air pressure inside the bottle. There is not any room for the air that you are trying to force inside the bottle so the balloon is impossible to inflate.

If you would like to try a fun variation on this experiment prepare a second plastic pop bottle. Drill a small hole near the bottom of the bottle and insert the balloon so it appears that the two containers are identical. As you demonstrate the experiment with your bottle, the balloon will inflate as air escapes through the hole. When the kids try it with their bottles they will not have any luck. This will help facilitate the understanding of the concept.

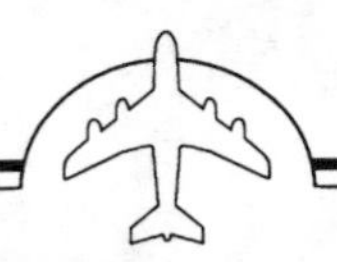

Friendly Bottle

the concept

A 16 oz. pop bottle that has been heated in a boiling water bath is placed firmly against the cheek. As the air inside cools, the bottle appears to "kiss" the student.

the materials

1 16 oz. pop bottle
1 hot plate
1 large steamer or other kitchen pan
water
1 pair of tongs
1 pair of garden gloves

the experiment

1. Fill the pan with water and heat it until it is near boiling. Place the bottle or bottles that you are going to use in the pan and let them heat up for about three minutes.

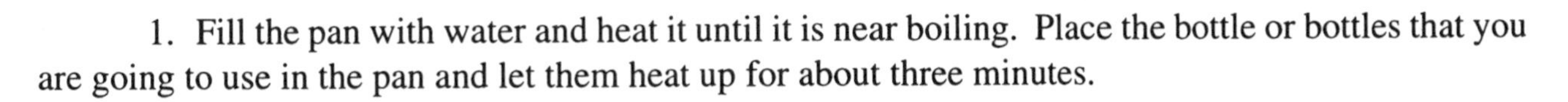

2. Remove the bottles with the tongs and have the kids hold the bottles, using the gloves if the bottles are too hot, next to their cheeks.

3. Let the bottle cool as it is held to the cheek and observe what happens.

the explanation

The skin acts as a natural seal for the bottle. As the air inside the bottle cools, it takes up less space. This is because the molecules have less energy and are slowing down. This creates an area of lower pressure inside the bottle. Because the inside of the student's mouth is at room pressure, probably 14.7 pounds per square inch, give or take, the pressure inside the mouth is greater than the pressure in the bottle. The difference in pressure pushes the skin of the mouth into the bottle. A kiss, if you will.

If the kids guess that the bottle sucks the skin into the bottle because it is hot, beat them with a stick and read them Rule #1 again.

Dueling Plungers

the concept

Two toilet plungers are placed nose to nose and squished together. Air pressure is responsible for keeping them together once the end of one of them is released.

the materials

2 toilet plungers
2 arms attached to the same body, hands preferable
air

the experiment

1. Take two toilet plungers and shove them together.

2. Release one of the handles and hold both plungers up with one hand. Assume the Three Musketeers position.

the explanation

As the two plungers are squished together, the air is squished out of the plungers. Because the plungers want to return to their natural shape, due to the elastic nature of the rubber, the air pressure on the inside of the plungers is now lowered. The higher pressure on the outside keeps the two halves pushed together.

Light Air • Heavy Air

the concept

An aquarium is divided in half by a piece of heavy cardboard. One side is filled with hot water and dyed red, representing a warm air mass; the other side is filled with cold water and dyed blue, representing a cool air mass. When the center divider is removed, the two "air masses" meet and the warm layer winds up on top and the cool layer winds up on the bottom.

the materials

1 10 gallon aquarium
1 bottle of red food coloring
1 bottle of blue food coloring
hot water
cold water
1 piece of cardboard

the experiment

1. Place the cardboard smack in the middle of the aquarium. The tighter the fit, the better the experiment will work.
2. Pour boiling hot water in one side of the aquarium until it comes close to the top. Add a couple of drops of red food coloring. This represents your warm air mass.
3. Do the same thing on the other side with cold water and add blue food coloring. This is your cold air mass.
4. When all the contestants are ready, pull the cardboard divider up out of the aquarium and observe what happens to the two "air masses."

the explanation

The warm water molecules have a lot of energy so they are spread way out. This makes them less dense. On the other hand, the cold water molecules are snuggling together to stay warm. They are extremely dense by comparison. When the divider is lifted, the cold water, being more dense, heads to the bottom of the tank, and the warm water, being less dense, to the top. The food coloring just identifies where each of the two different layers wind up.

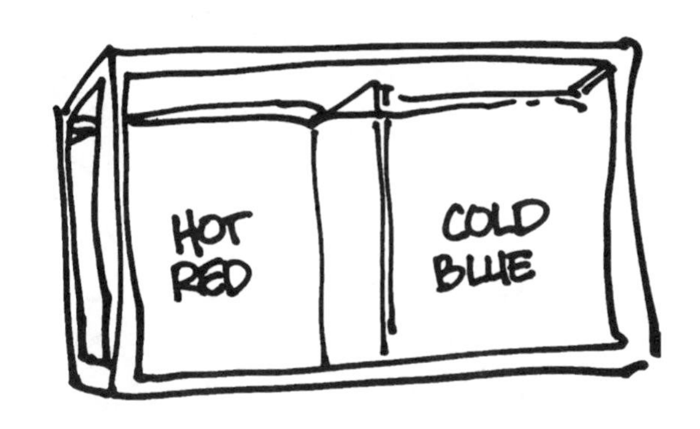

Bernoulli's Law

Bernoulli was an Italian physicist who figured out the physics behind flight. The law is fairly simple to understand, and even easier to illustrate with the activities in this section. He discovered that **the faster a fluid travels over a surface, the less time it has to push on that surface**. Air behaves just like a fluid so there is a direct correlation.

The best way to introduce the idea is to have the kids line up, walk over to the wall, and push on it. They will be able to push as hard as they want. Then have them line up again and walk the length of the wall while they try to push on it as they go. They can still push on the wall, but not as hard as if they are just standing there. Finally, have them run along the wall and try to push at the same time. They are so busy going forward that they have very little time, if any at all, to push on the wall. The faster that they move along the wall, the less time they have to push on the wall. Bernoulli's Law in physical terms that they can understand.

Just what this means for airplanes is illustrated below. The shape of an airplane wing is critical to the ability of the plane to generate lift and fly. The distance across the top of the wing must be longer than the distance on the underside of the wing. When the wing is traveling through the air at a fast enough speed, the air moving over the wing is moving quite a bit faster than the air moving under the wing. The faster the air travels, the less pressure it exerts on the wing. If the air traveling under the wing is moving slower, it exerts more pressure. We call this difference in pressure, lift. And now, the experiments ...

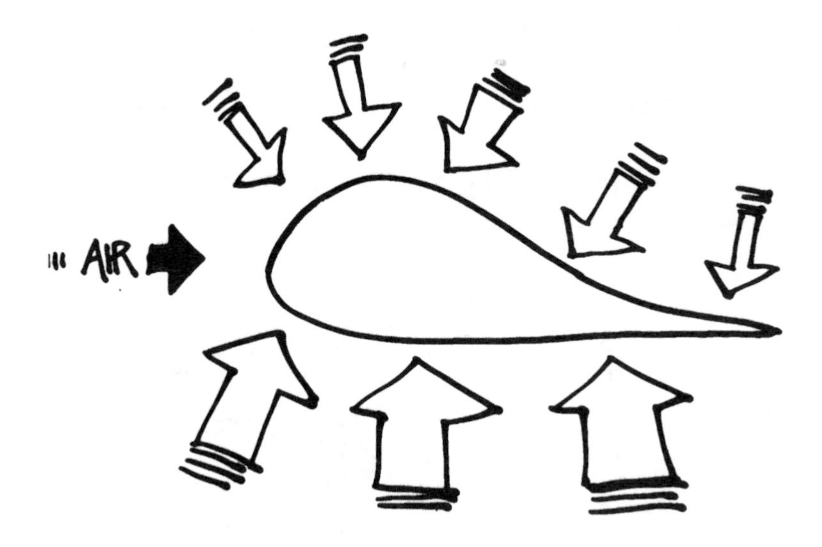

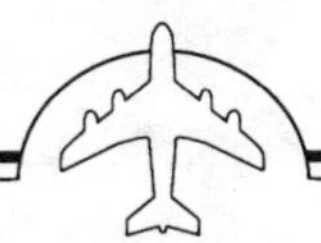

The Flying Sheet

the concept

A sheet of paper is held up to the lower lip and the student blows down across the top of the paper. The paper rises rather than presses against the chest.

the materials

1 sheet of paper
1 pair of lips and lungs

FRONT VIEW

the experiment

1. Have the kids hold a sheet of paper to their bottom lip like the kid in the cartoon. They are to imagine what will happen to the paper when they blow down and across the top of the paper. Their choices are that it will hit them in the chest, stay exactly where it is, or bounce up and hit them in the nose.

2. Once all the predictions are in, have them experiment and then discuss the results.

the explanation

The paper is surrounded by air and air pressure on both sides. When the kids start to blow air across the top of the page, the air that is pushing on that side does not have as much time to stop and push on the sheet. The air on the bottom is not moving as fast so it has more time to push. The sheet lifts and may hit the kid in the nose.

Card Bridge

the concept

An index card is suspended between two books. When the student blows under the card, it bends downward toward the table rather than upward.

SIDE VIEW

the materials

1 index card
2 thick books
1 kid with lungs

the experiment

1. Place two books about five inches apart on a table. Set the index card on top of the books so that just the ends of the index card rest on the books and the bulk of the card is over the open space. Use the illustration to the right as a guide.

MATH
HISTORY
TOP VIEW

2. Ask the kids to predict what will happen when they blow between the two books and underneath the card. The choices are: one, the card will remain unchanged; two, it will fly off the books and onto the table; and three, it will bend down toward the table. Have the kids experiment and discuss their results.

the explanation

Once again, the card is surrounded by air and air pressure on both sides. When the kids start to blow air under the card, the air that is pushing on that side does not have as much time to stop and push. The air on top of the card is not moving as fast, so it has more time to push. The card gently bends downward as a result of the difference in air pressure.

The reverse is true of the cloth top on a Jeep. As the Jeep moves down the road the air inside the vehicle is still, the air outside the vehicle is zipping along the top. The air inside has time to push, the outside does not. The top is pushed upward by the air inside the Jeep.

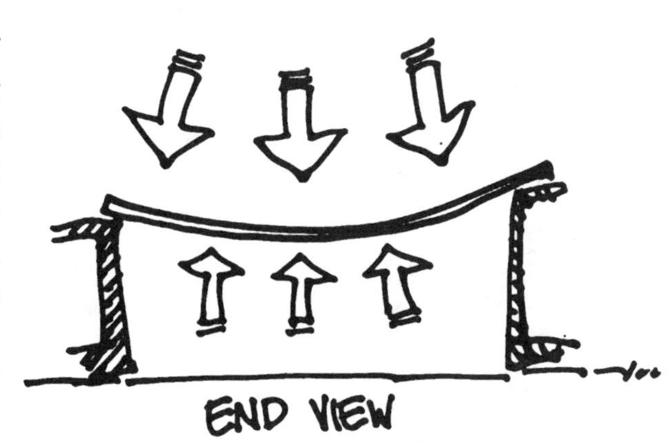

Funnel Puzzles

the concept

There are two activities using funnels and ping pong balls. Each demonstrates that the ball will not do something that we think it should.

the materials

1 funnel
1 ping pong ball
1 kid

the experiment

1. Have the kids place the funnel in their mouths like the picture to the upper right. Place a ping pong ball inside the funnel and then ask the kids to predict what will happen when they blow into the funnel. The choices are: one, the ball will remain unchanged; two, the ball will pop out of the funnel; and three, it will be pushed deeper into the funnel core.

2. Have the kids experiment and discuss their results.

3. When they have finished with that aspect of the experiment, challenge them to flip the funnel upside down and find a way to keep the ball inside without using fingers, tape, glue, or any other adhesives. The bottom illustration will give you a clue.

the explanation

There is air completely surrounding the ball. As you blow into the funnel, the air immediately above the opening of the spout is moving much faster than the rest of the air around the ball. This means that the ball will be pushed toward the opening where the air is moving at all times, whether the funnel is upside down or right side up.

Paper Tent

the concept

A tent is made out of a piece of paper. When the student blows through the tent, it bends inward rather than outward.

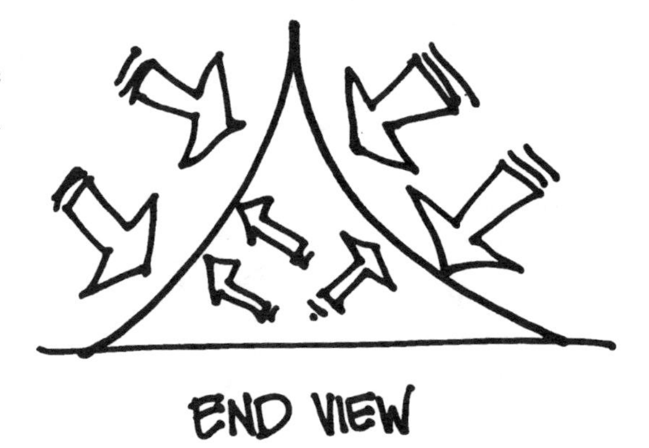

the materials

1 sheet of copy paper
1 healthy set of lungs

the experiment

1. Have the kids fold the paper in half and make a paper tent. Set the tent up using the illustration to the right as a guide.

2. Ask the kids to predict what will happen when they blow into the tent. The choices are: one, it will remain unchanged; two, the sides will inflate and the tent will appear to get larger; or three, it will bend down toward the table.

3. Have the kids experiment and discuss their results.

the explanation

The paper is surrounded by air and air pressure on both sides. When the kids start to blow air through the tent, the air that is pushing on that side does not have as much time to stop and push on the paper. The air on the outside of the tent is not moving as fast so it has more time to push. The tent appears to collapse.

Airball

the concept

A ping pong ball is placed inside a paper cone attached to a hair dryer. As the cone is tipped, the ball remains in place at an angle where you would expect it to fall out.

the materials

1 hair dryer
1 ping pong ball
1 roll of tape
1 sheet of paper
1 kid

the experiment

1. Wrap the paper around the nozzle of the hair dryer and tape it in place.

2. Ask the kids to predict what will happen when the hair dryer is turned on and a ping pong ball is placed in the top of the cone. Ask them to speculate how far you can tip the cone before the ball will fall out.

3. Have the kids experiment and discuss their results.

the explanation

The air is moving along the sides of the ping pong ball and not on the top or the bottom. The stationary air on the top and the bottom acts as a retainer for the ball. As you tip the cone sideways, the stationary air keeps the ball in place.

Upside Down Spool

the concept

A paper disk with a pin inserted inside it is placed in the center of a sewing spool. When the student blows through the center of the spool, the paper remains pushed up against the spool rather than falling to the ground.

the materials

1 piece of paper
1 empty sewing spool
1 pin
1 pair of scissors
1 drawing compass

the experiment

1. Stretch the compass out so that it will make a 5-inch circle. Draw the circle on the paper and cut it out using the scissors.

2. Insert the pin in the middle of the paper disk. Place the pin inside the spool and ask the kids to predict what will happen when they blow down into the other end of the spool. The choices are: one, it will remain unchanged; two, it will float down to the floor; and three, it will be pushed up toward the spool.

3. Have the kids experiment and discuss their results.

the explanation

There is air pressure pushing down and up onto the spool. As the kids blow down into the spool, they are creating a fast moving layer of air on top of the disk. This lowers the pressure on top of the paper, but the bottom remains unchanged. This difference in air pressure pushes the disk up toward the spool.

Kissing Balloons

the concept

Two balloons are suspended from string. The student blows between them and they come together and "kiss."

the materials

2 balloons
2 pieces of string, at least 18 inches long
1 set of lungs

the experiment

1. Blow up both the balloons, tie them off, and then attach a string to each one.

2. Ask the kids to predict what will happen when they blow between the two balloons. The choices are: one, they will remain unchanged; two, they will blow apart and away from each other; and three, they will come toward each other and bump. Or kiss, if you prefer.

3. Have the kids experiment and discuss their results.

the explanation

The balloons are surrounded by air and air pressure on all sides. When the kids start to blow air between them, the air that is pushing on that side does not have as much time to stop and push. The air on the outside of the balloons is not moving as fast so it has more time to push. The balloons bump into one another and appear to kiss.

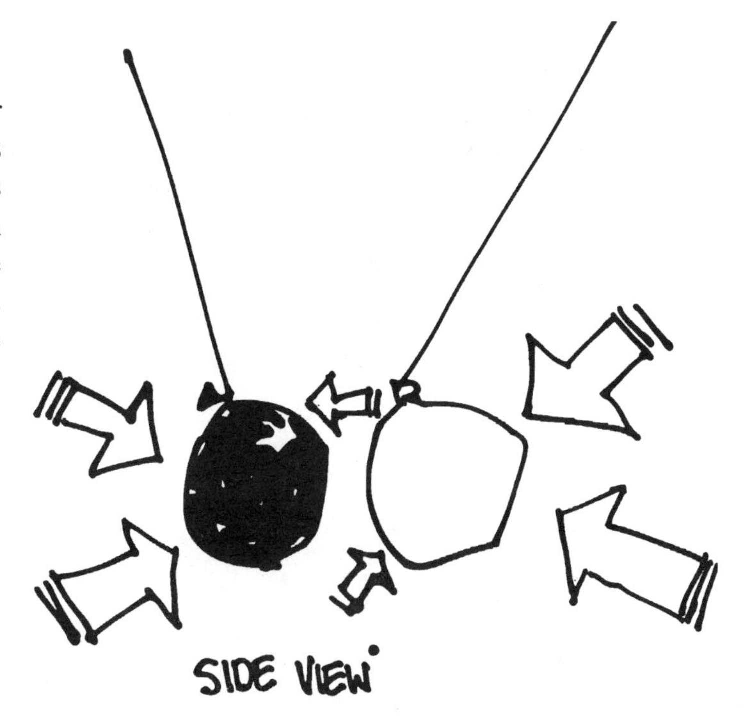

Sticky Papers

the concept

Two strips of newspaper are hung four inches apart. As the kids blow between them, the strips come together and touch.

the materials

1 sheet of newspaper
1 pair of scissors

the experiment

1. Cut two 1-inch wide strips from the newspaper; cut lengthwise so that the sheets are long and flimsy.

2. Ask the kids to predict what will happen when they blow between the two strips of paper. The choices are: one, they will remain unchanged; two, they will blow apart and away from each other; and three, they will come toward each other and bump or "stick" together.

3. Have the kids experiment and discuss their results.

the explanation

The strips of paper are surrounded by air and air pressure on all sides. When the kids start to blow air between them, the air that is pushing on that side does not have as much time to stop and push. The air on the outside of the strips is not moving as fast, so it has more time to push. The strips of paper appear to move toward one another and stick.

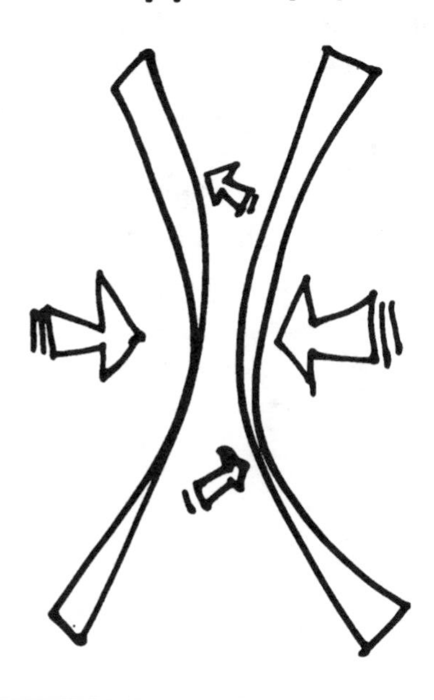

Thirsty Straw

the concept

A straw is placed inside a beaker of water. As the kids blow across the top of the straw, water rises into the straw. When the kids stop blowing, the water level inside the straw drops back down and remains the same as in the beaker.

the materials

1 drinking straw
1 400 ml beaker or drinking glass
water

the experiment

1. Unwrap the straw and place it in the beaker full of water. Have the kids observe the fact that the water level in the straw is the same as the water level in the beaker.

2. Ask the kids to predict what will happen when they blow across the top of the straw. The choices are: one, it will remain unchanged; two, the water level will get pushed down into the water; and three, the water level inside the straw will rise up higher than the water level in the beaker.

3. Have the kids experiment and discuss their results.

the explanation

At rest the air is pushing down on the surface of the water in the beaker and in the straw with equal force. When you blow across the top of the straw, the air immediately over the water in that small area begins to move faster and reduces the pressure on the water there. The pressure outside the straw remains the same, but is now greater than the pressure inside the straw and, consequently, pushes the water up the straw.

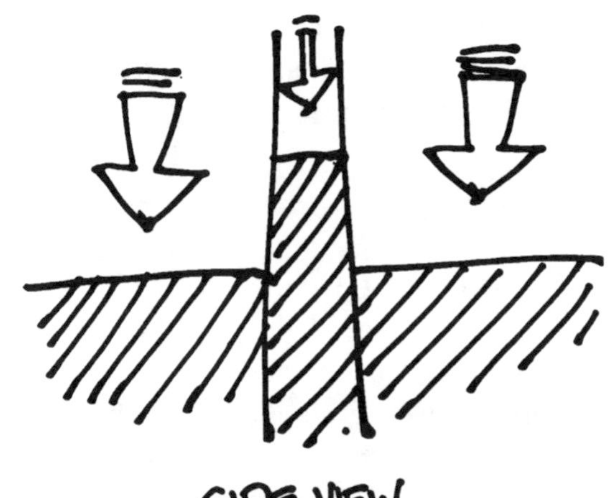

The Coke Can Trick

the concept

Just for the record, this is my favorite Bernoulli's Law experiment. You take a whole pile of naked straws and line them up roughly a half an inch apart. You take your basic soda can. I'm plugging Coke because my dad used to work for said Fortune 500 company. Place the two cans four inches apart on top of the straws. When you blow between the cans, they roll together and clink. No way, dude.

the materials

25 drinking straws (the number can vary, so experiment!)
2 empty Coke cans (Pepsi will do, if you must)
a lot of hot air

the experiment

1. Unwrap the straws and line them up on the table about a half an inch apart. The heavier the straw wall, the better they tend to work. I prefer McDonald's (a distributor of those fine Coke products) straws, but any heavy wall straw is fine.

2. Place the two cans on the straws anywhere from two to four inches apart. They just need to be in the middle of the straws so that they are free to roll.

3. Ask the kids to predict what will happen if you blow between the cans. If you have done any footwork up to this point, the kids will know that the two cans are going to be pushed together and clink. Blow between the cans and demonstrate Bernoulli's principle for the umpteenth time. Experiment with moving the straws different distances apart and see how far out you can go.

the explanation

As the air traveling between the cans increases in speed, the pressure that it exerts on the cans decreases. It doesn't have time to push on the cans. As a result, the air pressure on the outside, which remains constant, is now greater than the air pressure on the inside and pushes the cans together.

Flying Gizmos

What can I say? It's time to party.

Jet

materials

1 sheet of copy paper

construction instructions

1. Fold the page in half and then unfold it.

2. Grab the upper corner and fold it down into the middle of the page. Do the same thing for other side. You should now have something that looks like the outline of a house.

3. Grab the edges again and fold them over into the middle one more time. You now have a very steep "A" frame house.

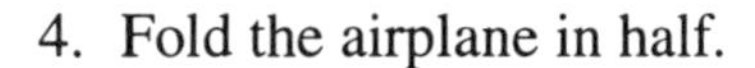

4. Fold the airplane in half.

5. The final fold is for the wings. The edge of the wing should be matched up perfectly with the bottom of the plane. If you want to give the plane even more stability, tape the wings together.

take off

This is one of those planes that your mother always warned you to be careful with because it could poke someone's eye out. Find a large open area and throw it as hard as you can.

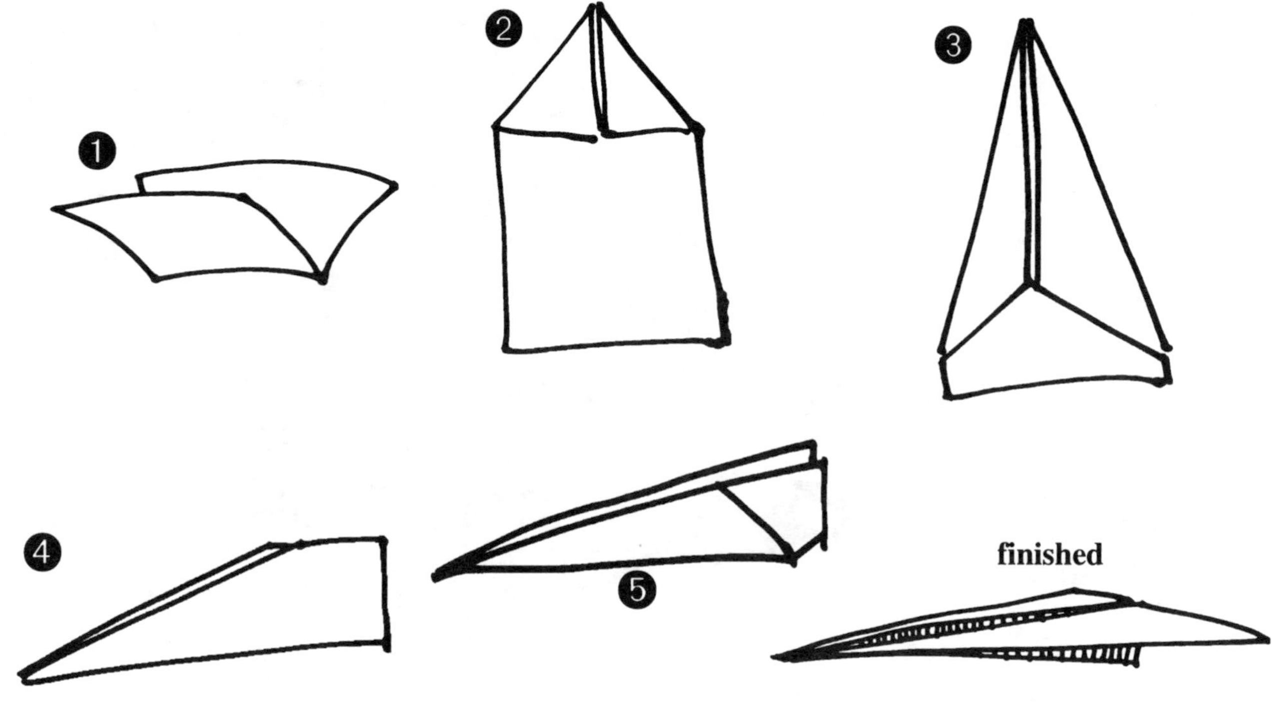

My Standard

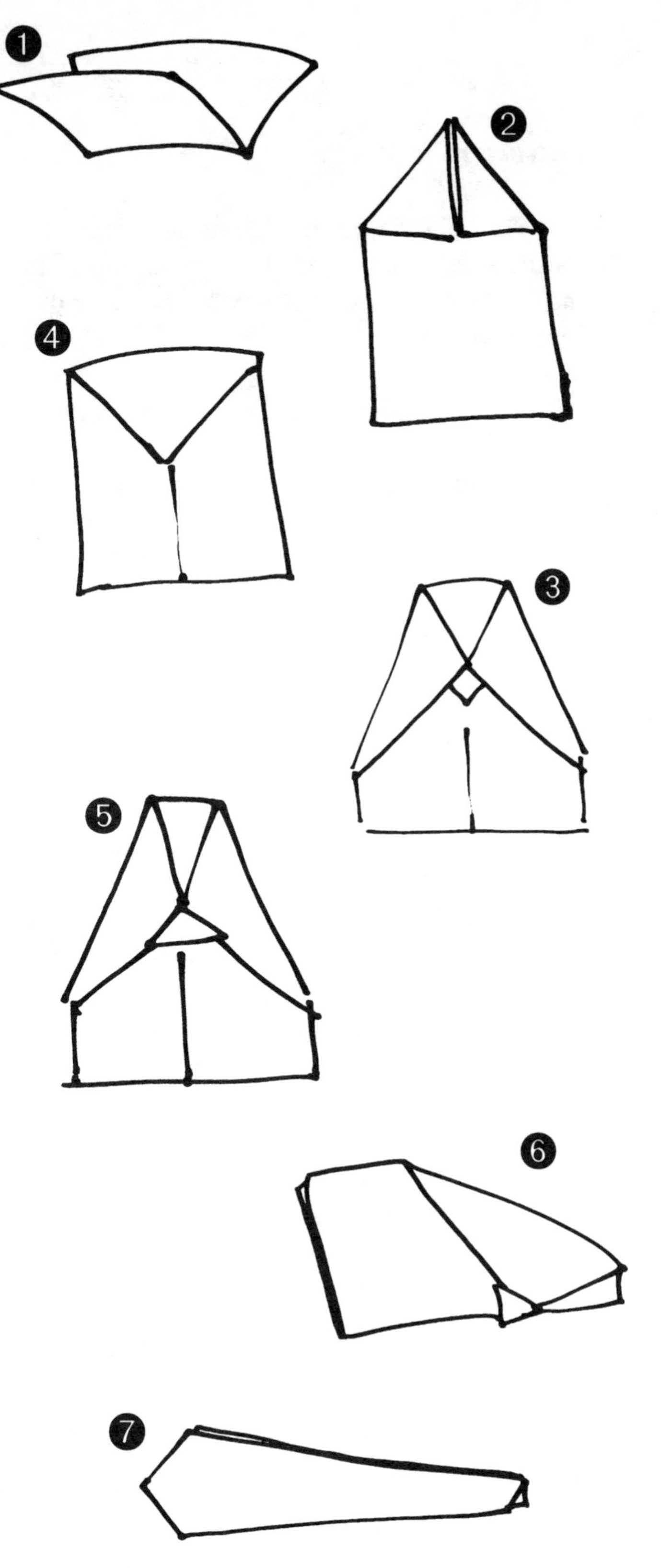

materials

1 sheet of copy paper

construction instructions

1. Fold the paper in half and unfold it.

2. Grab the upper corner and fold it down into the middle of the page. Do the same thing for the other side. You should now have something that looks like the outline of a house.

3. Fold the roof of the house completely over so that you now have a square.

4. Fold the upper right hand corner of the house to the center line of the square. It should be about two thirds of the way up from the bottom of the square. Do the same thing on the other side.

5. There is an odd shaped diamond that used to be the top of the roof on the house. Fold that up so that it holds the corners of fold number 4 down.

6. Fold the airplane in half so that the folds you have been making are exposed.

7. The wing is the final fold. The outer edge of the wing should be matched perfectly with the bottom of the airplane. If you would like to tape the top of the wings together, you may.

take off

I call it my standard because every kid has the airplane that they make and are especially good at constructing in elementary school. This is my favorite design. Once you have it together, a good firm toss will make it fly quite nicely. If you fold the back wings a little bit, it will influence the way the plane flies. I prefer the straight wing approach.

Trickster

materials

1 sheet of copy paper

construction instructions

1. Fold the upper edge of the plane over to the opposite side of the paper. Unfold and repeat the same thing for the other side. You now have an X in the middle of your page.

2. This is the tricky part. Grab the center of the X and fold it into the middle so that you have converted the page into another outline of a house. Use the illustrations.

3. Fold the tip of the roof of the house to the gutter.

4. Fold the airplane in half so that the folds are not showing.

5. Fold the wings down. The body of the airplane should be no more than a half an inch tall.

6. Fold the outer quarter inch of the airplane wing up into the air. Tape the two wings together at the center of the design.

7. Cut two small flaps out of the back of the wings in the sections illustrated. Use these to direct the movement of the plane.

take off

By bending the flaps on the back of the wing, you can get the plane to bank both left and right. If you bend both flaps the same way, you can get the plane to climb sharply into the atmosphere or biff it right into the dirt.

This plane, more than any others that may be out there, demonstrates the movement of the airplane in response to the air that it is traveling through. If you take time to refine your design, you can really get the thing to humm. Party on.

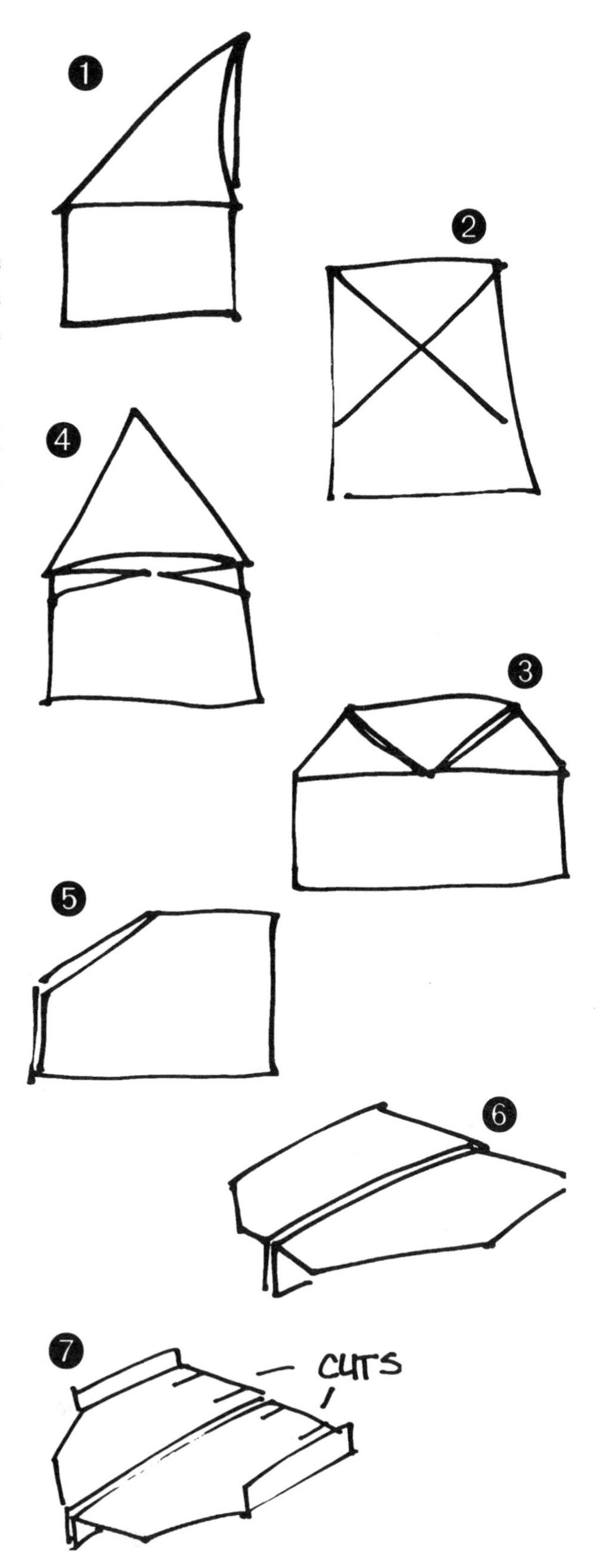

Two Loops

materials

1 sheet of copy paper
1 pair of scissors
1 roll of masking tape
1 drinking straw

construction instructions

1. Cut out two strips of paper similar in size to the two strips pictured to the right.

2. Tape them into two loops. You should have a large loop and a small loop.

3. Place a piece of tape at each end of the straw (after you have taken the wrapper off).

4. Slip the loops on either end of the straw and pat the tape down so that it holds the loops in place. The illustration should help you with this last direction.

5. Toss the plane small loop first.

take off

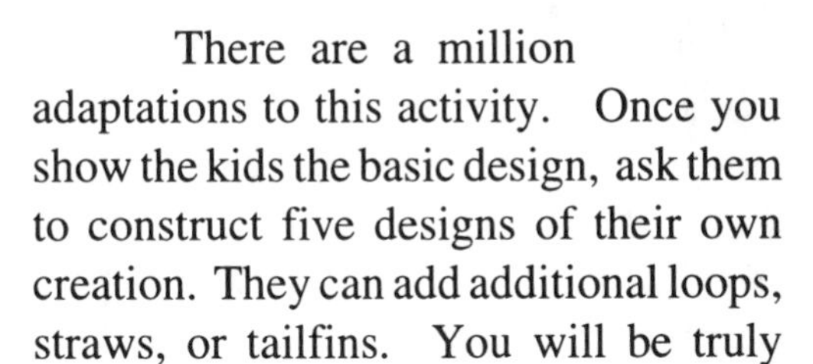

There are a million adaptations to this activity. Once you show the kids the basic design, ask them to construct five designs of their own creation. They can add additional loops, straws, or tailfins. You will be truly amazed.

Tubular 'Copter

materials

1 sheet of copy paper
1 pair of scissors

construction instructions

1. Using the design at the right, make a cut on all the solid lines. The dotted lines are where you should fold.

2. Holding the design upright, fold strip A toward you and strip B away from you. Place the design on the table.

3. Fold the sides of the helicopter into the middle of the design the same way that you would make a legal fold.

4. The final fold is to hold the helicopter together. Take the bottom half inch or so and fold it up. This is your landing gear.

A B

take off

To fly this, all you have to do is drop it from your fingers. There are a couple of glitches that you can trouble shoot without any problems. One, if the kids try to fly the helicopter with the rotors (flaps) pointing down, there can be too much air resistance to overcome and the copter just tumbles instead of twirling. Two, if the rotors are too long on some of the free hand designs, they will also just tumble. Snip the blades and make them a little shorter.

The Wing

materials

1 sheet of copy paper

construction instructions

1. Make a copy of the design below and cut it out along the solid lines.
2. Fold each dotted section onto the next section as if it were a flat roll. Tape the last fold to the paper that has not been folded.
3. Lightly crease the airplane so that it has a slight U-shaped upward bend.

take off

This is an incredibly simple plane to construct, but is much trickier to fly. Hold the airplane between your thumb and forefinger and toss it with a gentle horizontal motion.

Challenge the kids to modify the plane by lengthening, fattening, or otherwise changing the design to get it to fly better.

Your Original Design

materials

construction instructions

1.

2.

3.

4.

5.

6.

7.

take off

Balloon Rocket

materials

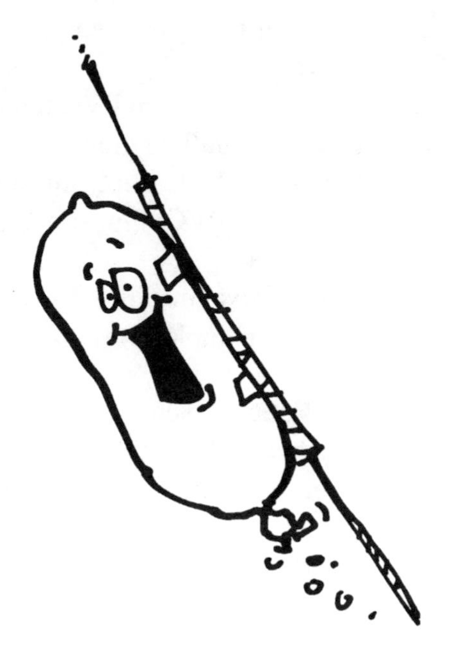

1 straw
1 roll of string
1 roll of masking tape
1 large, rubber balloon
2 kids

construction instructions

1. Thread the straw onto the string, and tie the string to two solid objects that are far apart, like door knobs...

2. Attach two pieces of masking tape at the one-third and the two-thirds points on the straw.

3. Blow the balloon up and stick it to the tape that is on the straw. Do not tie the balloon off.

4. When all interested parties are ready, launch the balloon by releasing it.

take off

There are all sorts of adaptations. You can add extra balloons, give the rocket a load to carry, or launch it straight up, across, or down.

Water Rocket

materials

1 2 liter pop bottle (empty)
water
5 feet of half-inch PVC tubing, sections include: 3 in., 7 in., 13 in.(2), and 24 in.
1 can of caulk or glue
1 T joint (PVC, slip, slip, slip)
1 T joint (PVC, slip, slip, screw)
3 end caps
1 tire valve, medium
1 4-inch nipple
drill and bit
1 plastic pipe cutter
1 elbow (PVC, slip, slip)
1 bicycle pump or air compressor

construction instructions

The actual layout for the launcher is on page 43. You will need to drill a hole in one of the end caps using a bit that is large enough to allow the tire valve through. Use the drawing on page 43 to help you assemble the launcher.

take off

Add a little water to the bottle and wiggle the bottle rocket onto the launcher. The amount of water isn't important at first, but a third will do for those of you that need a measurement. Attach the pump and start to pump air into the rocket. You will be able to see the air gurgle up into the rocket. As the pressure inside increases, the rocket will be more and more susceptible to launch. Keep pumping and it will eventually shoot off the stand and up into the air.

Water Rocket

Once you have launched your rocket a couple of times and get the hang of it, there are a couple of things that you can do to influence the performance. The first is that you should figure out the right proportion of water to air to give your rocket the optimal boost. Use the data table down below to record the data that you collect.

Your rocket has a capacity of two liters, which means that it can hold two liters of fluid. This is also 2000 milliliters. Using either a beaker or graduated cylindar, fill and shoot your rocket with the mixtures listed below. Check the box that seems to fit the correct height.

Mixture		Estimated Height				
Water (ml)	Air (ml)	Low	Med	Med High	High	Way High
0	2000					
500	1500					
750	1250					
1000	1000					
750	1250					
500	1500					
2000	0					

questions

1. Which mixture do you think is best to launch your rocket the highest?
2. How would making a nose cone affect the ability of the rocket to fly? Fins? Try it.
3. What other factors influence the ability of the rocket to fly?

Water Rocket

Pattern for the Rocket Launcher

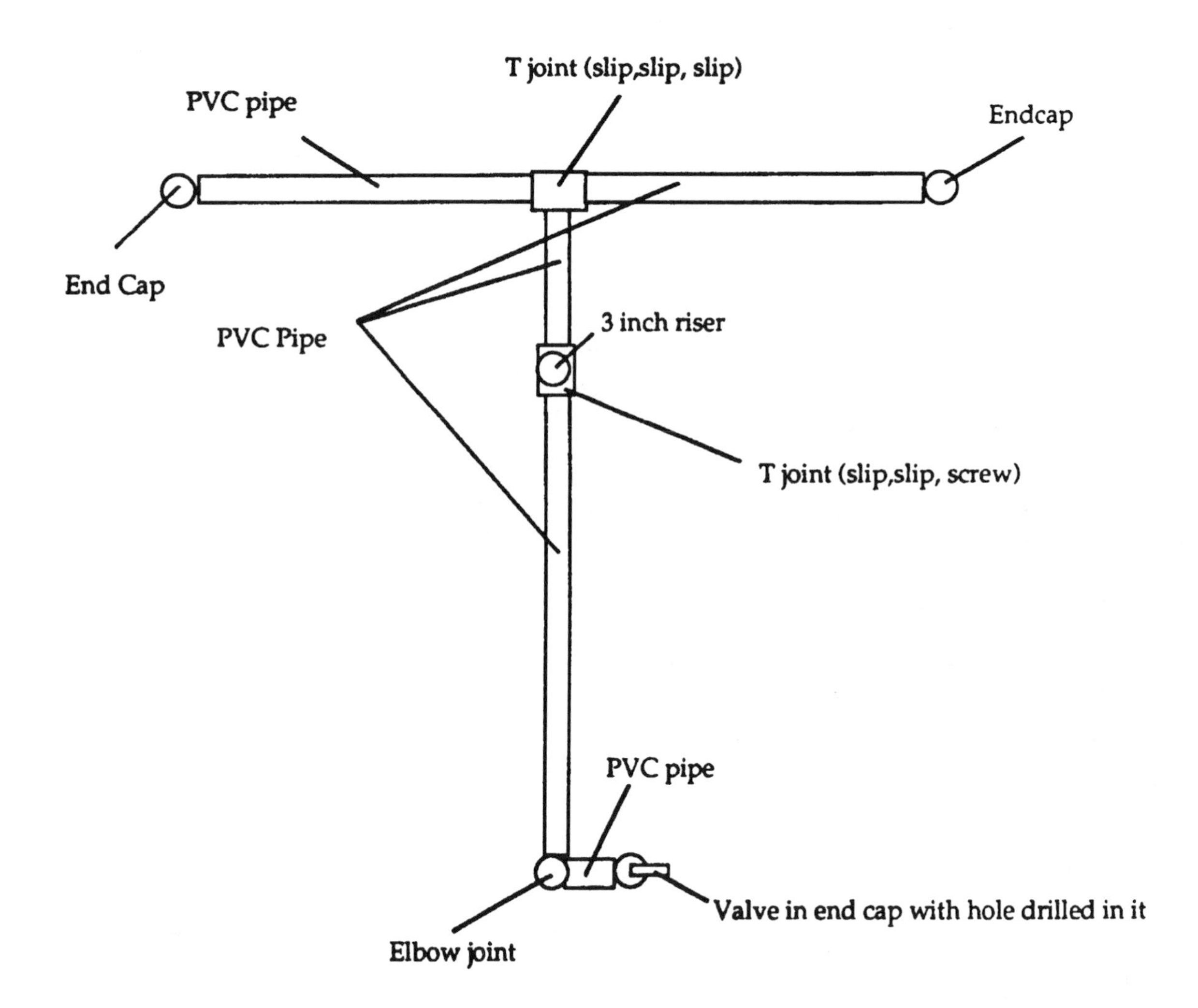

Solid Fuel Rocket

materials

1 Estes Mosquito rocket kit
1 3 ft length of sturdy welding rod
1 30 ft length of bell wire (check your hardware store)
1 wire cutter/stripper
1 6 V lantern battery
1 electrical switch
2 alligator clips
1 large, open grassy area

construction instructions

1. Build the rocket according to the directions in the kit.

2. Shove the welding rod into the ground and slide the rocket onto it. Make sure that you are a long way from buildings, wooded areas, and old ladies.

3. Strip the ends of the bell wire and attach one alligator clip to each end. Clip the other end of each of the alligator clips to the wires coming out of the rocket motors.

4. Attach the other end of the bell wire (after you have stripped it) to the switch. Make sure the switch is open.

5. Attach the other two alligator clips to the battery and then to the switch. If all of this is too confusing, you can buy a rocket launching kit for about $10 at your local hobby store. Rough it first.

6. When everyone is out of the way and ready to launch, throw the switch.

Bernoulli's Notes

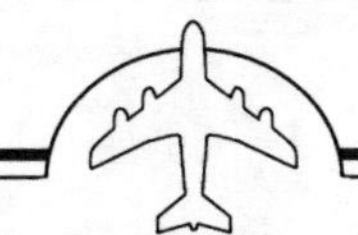

Bernoulli's Notes

Bernoulli's Notes